The World of ANDY CAPP

cartoons by Reg Smythe

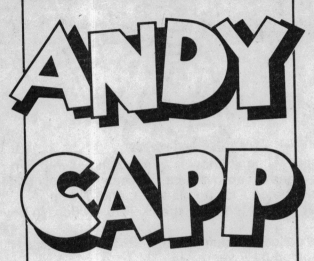

KU-656-876

Mirror Publications

INTRODUCTION

Well, it's the thought that counts (Front Cover).
Here we go with another selection of the lad's antics - I don't know how she puts up with him.

The other day someone said he seemed to be showing signs of improvement, but I can't say I've noticed it myself. I'm glad Andy didn't hear the remark, he'd be devastated - losing his touch and all that.

I've never thought that people do change, anyway. They just get more like themselves - which isn't a very merry Christmas thought for Flo.

She was talking about spending the two days Christmas holiday at some nice hotel. You know, miss all the chores, no worries, have a real enjoyable time. She's fancied it for years.

But it's off again - he insists on coming.

All the best.

Reg. Smythe.

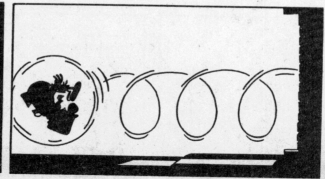

X232

X233

X240

X241

X308

I'M NEVER GOING TO BE IN THE COMPANY OF THAT GRAHAM AGAIN~!

HE ACCUSED ME OF NOT PAYING MY TURN! THAT'S THE FINISH, THE END, *FINITO*~!

A PITY, THAT. WE'RE INVITED TO THEIR ANNIVERSARY PARTY NEXT WEEK — THEY ALWAYS HAVE A GOOD 'DO'

WELL, ALL RIGHT, THEN. I'M NOT ONE TO BE VINDICTIVE — BUT DIRECTLY AFTER THE PARTY

FLO! AFTER ALL THIS TIME~!

HELLO THERE, DORA~

I'VE JUST MET ANDY IN THERE. HE LOOKS JUST THE SAME AS HE DID TWENTY YEARS AGO—

PLASTERED?

WHAT ELSE?

- X309 -

SHE ENJOYED THAT

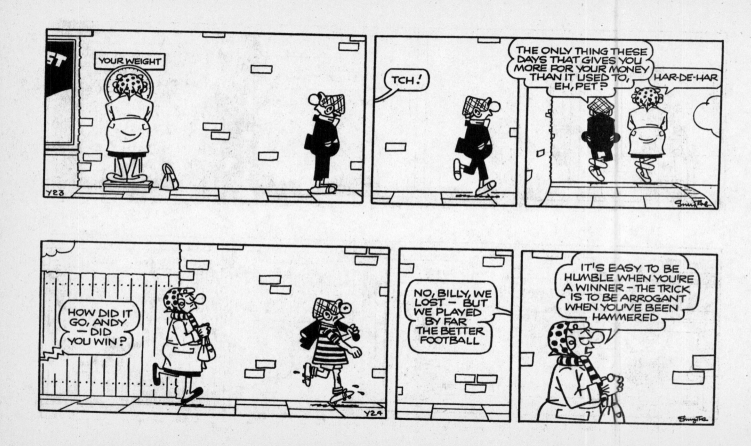

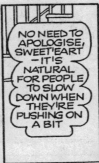

'BYE, MUM, TAKE CARE!

I FELT I HAD TO TREAT MY MOTHER TO HER BUS FARE HOME —

ANY OTHER SON-IN-LAW WOULD'VE LET HER STAY OVER — IT'S A LONG AND TIRING JOURNEY AT THIS TIME OF NIGHT

Y69

AND SO IT FLIPPIN' WELL OUGHT TO BE FOR *THAT* KIND OF MONEY!

WATCH IT, PERCY, YOU KNOW WHAT HE'S LIKE!

ANYTHING GOES IN *THIS* LEAGUE —

AND THE FIRST THING TO *GO* IS USUALLY MY NERVE

GRRR

Y60

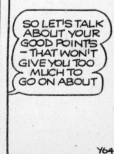

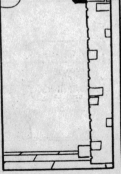

Y105

SPLOSH

I'M GETTING TOO IMMERSED IN MY WORK — CAPP'S ENTIRE LIFE FLASHED BEFORE MY EYES —!

Smythe

IT'S JUST OCCURRED TO ME, FLO — WE HAVEN'T BEEN IN THAT PUB SINCE WE WERE EIGHTEEN YEARS OLD

THAT'S RIGHT, RUBE. WE HAD OUR FIRST DRINK IN THERE

Y106

WE HAD SUCH HIGH HOPES AND BIG IDEAS IN THOSE DAYS — WHERE DID IT ALL GO WRONG?

OFFHAND, I CAN THINK OF A COUPLE OF REASONS —

♪ DEAR OLD PALS —!! ♪

Smythe

MODERN TIMES — THE WOMEN TALK POLITICS AND THE MEN TALK RECIPES

WON'T BE TOO LONG, PET — I'M JUST JOGGING DOWN TO THE SLIMMING CLUB

GOOD HEAVENS, FLO! YOU'RE NOT GOING OUT LIKE THAT, ARE YOU?

?

SLIM FIRST AND *THEN* WEAR IT — RIGHT?

RIGHT

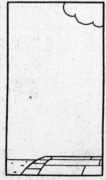

THAT'S POOR FLO'S HUSBAND

IN THIS DISTRICT A MAN IS KNOWN BY THE COMPANY THAT KEEPS HIM

DON'T FORGET, NOW, YOU PROMISED TO TAKE ME OUT FOR A DRINK TONIGHT

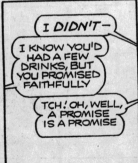
I DIDN'T—
I KNOW YOU'D HAD A FEW DRINKS, BUT YOU PROMISED FAITHFULLY
TCH! OH, WELL, A PROMISE IS A PROMISE

WE'RE ALL ALLOWED ONE LITTLE LIE, EH?

DO YOU LOVE ME, PET?

VERY MUCH SO

HOW MUCH?

I'LL SHOW YOU —

Y159

THERE'S MY SAVINGS BOOK – CHECK THE WITHDRAWALS

TCH, IT DOESN'T TAKE MUCH THESE DAYS, DOES IT, AMY?

YOUNG EDNA AND HER HUSBAND HAVE SPLIT UP

FLIPPIN' KIDS. THEY'VE ONLY BEEN MARRIED FIVE MINUTES — WHAT WAS THE TROUBLE?

WHO KNOWS —

Y160

ALL THEY NEED FOR A DIVORCE THESE DAYS IS A WEDDING

ISN'T IT THE TRUTH

GRR-RRR

A WORD OF ADVICE, CHALKIE — DON'T BEAT HIM AT SNOOKER TONIGHT

RELAX. YOU'RE GETTING QUITE PARANOID ABOUT YOUR MISSUS WALKING IN ON US

YOU CERTAINLY ARE

I SUPPOSE I AM, REALLY...

...BUT THEN AGAIN, JUST BECAUSE I'M PARANOID DOESN'T MEAN THAT SHE WON'T WALK IN ON US...

I GIVE UP

© 1990 Mirror Publications Ltd. First published in Great Britain by Mirror Publications Ltd, 3rd Floor, Greater London House, Hampstead Road, London NW1 7QQ. Printed in Great Britain by Spottiswoode Ballantyne Printers Ltd, Colchester and London. Distributed by IPC Marketforce, King's Reach Tower, Stamford Street, London SE1 9LS.

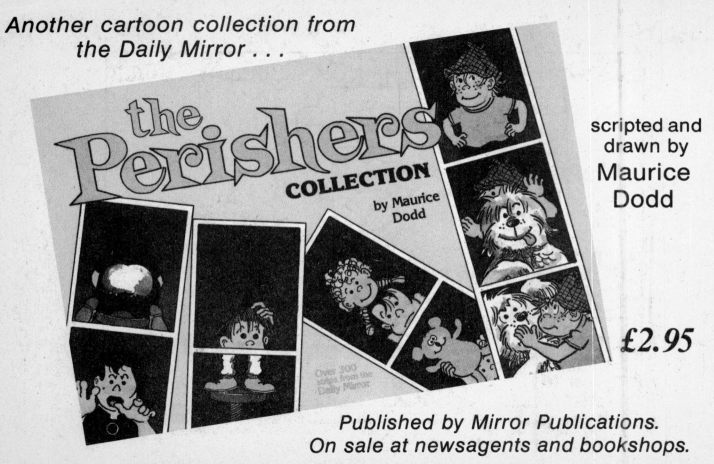

Another cartoon collection from the Daily Mirror . . .

the **Perishers** COLLECTION

by Maurice Dodd

scripted and drawn by **Maurice Dodd**

Over 200 strips from the Daily Mirror

£2.95

**Published by Mirror Publications.
On sale at newsagents and bookshops.**

Also available direct from publisher price £3.25 (inc. postage) Address - see imprint.